This book belongs to:

_____

To my husband Jason and my two beautiful children Emerson & Wyatt... you are my inspiration for this book & for always!

For more information contact
Stacy Seltzer at mymomandthesun@gmail.com
ISBN: 9798747192843 *Independently published*

My Mom and the Sun

By Stacy Seltzer

Emerson took a deep breath and blew one of her long blonde curls out of her face.

Her teacher, Mrs. Fox, had just finished the math lesson for the day. Now they were moving on to her least favorite subject, science.

To start the science lesson, Mrs. Fox asked the class to tell her what they knew about the sun.

Several students raised their hands, and one by one, they told her some of their favorite facts about the sun.

Emerson watched closely as Mrs. Fox wrote each fact on the board. The more the teacher wrote, the more this confused Emerson.

She couldn't help but wonder if teachers could make mistakes?

THE SUN

1- The sun makes plants grow which gives u food to eat.

2- The Sun rises to wake us up and sets when its time for bed.

3- The Sun keeps everyone on earth alive

4- The Sun is the center of our solar system.

5- The Sun keeps all planets in line.

6- The Sun warms the earth.

7- The sun is one of many stars but is most important to earth.

After thinking for a little, Emerson shot her arm in the air and started waving it back and forth. Soon, Mrs. Fox noticed her excitement and asked, "Emerson, do you have a question?"

Emerson nervously nodded, but smiled and answered, "Are you sure that list is about the sun?"

Mrs. Fox looked back at the board and jokingly replied, "Yes, what else would it be about?"

"Well," Emerson politely objected, "It sounds to me like you are actually talking about my mom."

A few kids in the class began to laugh, but Emerson remained serious; so Mrs. Fox invited Emerson to the front of the room to explain.

As soon as Emerson reached the board, she pointed to the first line.

"ONE", Emerson suggested, confidently. "The sun makes plants grow which gives us food to eat, but my mom has a garden where she grows vegetables that she uses to cook meals for my family every day."

Emerson looked around the room noticing all eyes glued on her, so she gulped and quickly moved on.

"TWO. The sun rises to wake us up and sets when it's time for bed, but my mom is the one who always wakes me up in the morning and puts me to bed every night."

Big smiles started to form on her classmate's faces. This made Emerson so happy that she jumped right to the next fact.

"THREE. The sun keeps everyone on earth alive, but my mom is the one who keeps me alive every day."

Next, Emerson put her hand on her heart and said, "FOUR. The sun is the center of our solar system, but my dad told me that my mom is the center of our whole family."

Emerson soon noticed more and more kids nodding their heads, and so she knew she needed to keep going.

"FIVE," she stated with a smile on her face. "It says the sun keeps all the planets in line, but my mom is definitely the one who keeps me in line and out of trouble!"

The class briefly exploded with laughter, but quieted down quickly as Emerson proudly shouted, "SIX! The sun warms the earth, but my mom is always there to make sure I am comfy and warm."

Emerson stood a little taller and took a deep breath as she got to the last item on the board.

"SEVEN. The sun is one of many stars, but is most important to earth, and I know there are many moms out there, but for me, my mom is the most special of them all!"

The teacher and the class were suddenly silent as they thought about what Emerson had just said.

Each child was comparing every item on the board to their own mom, while thinking about all the wonderful things their moms did for them each day.

Mrs. Fox was even thinking about her own mom, and the many memories she had from when she was the same age as the children in the classroom.

All of a sudden, Emerson's face lit up, and she smiled so big that her cheeks hurt. It finally made sense.

"Wait," she shouted. "This list is about my mom AND the sun!"

And with a little giggle, she walked back to her desk and whispered to herself, "I can't believe it, my mom is just like the sun."

Every face in the class joined Emerson with the same joyful smile, because in that moment, they all knew that their moms were also just like the sun.

Made in the USA
Middletown, DE
04 May 2021